Eddy has put some new letter magnets
Draw over the dotted lines inside Eddy

X

y

Colour the **x** letters blue.

Colour the **y** letters red.

Colour the **z** letters yellow.

Colour the **q** letters green.

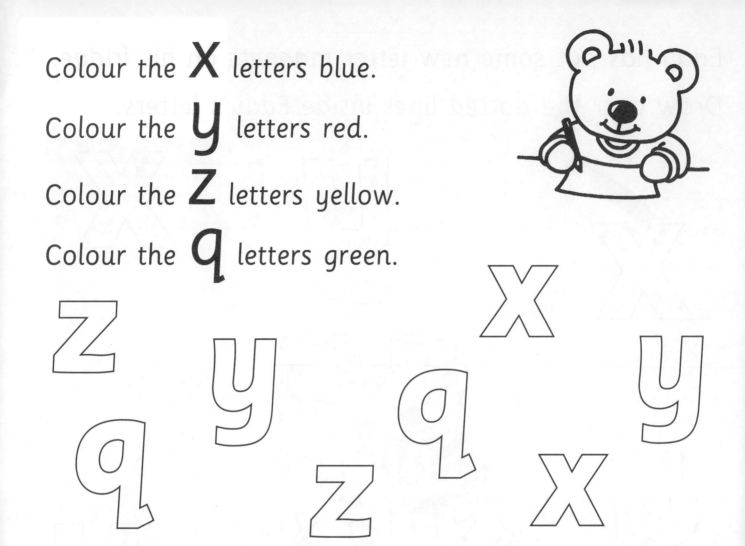

Eddy has written some letters for you to trace.

Draw some more of each letter on the line.

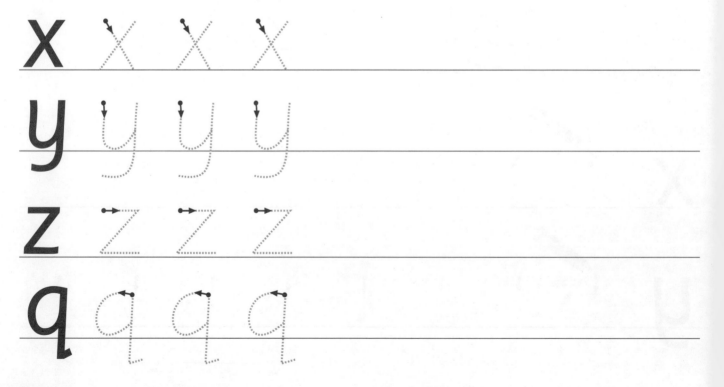

4

Pre-School **Nursery Writing Book 5**

Schofield & Sims

NURSERY WRITING 5

Name

Eddy has drawn some letters.

Draw over the dotted lines inside Eddy's letters.

q

z

Eddy is having fun on the bouncy castle.
Colour the picture using the colour that goes
with each letter.

S = green t = yellow U = pink V = brown

W = orange X = red Y = blue Z = black

Help Eddy to finish his jigsaw.
Match the letters to the spaces.

q

t

v

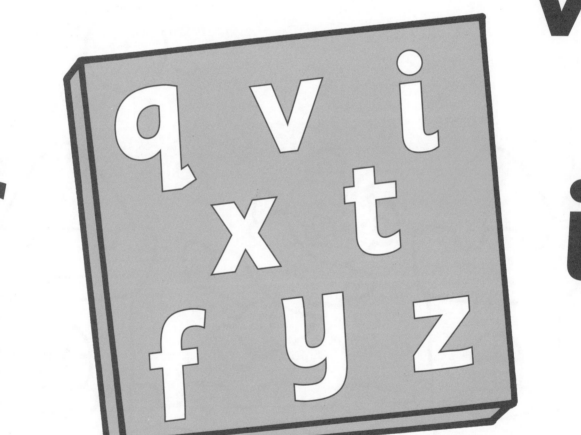

f

i

x

z

y

Look at the pictures and think of the start of the words.

Colour the **y** pictures blue.

Colour the **z** pictures pink.

Colour the **p** pictures purple.

Colour the **b** pictures orange.

p b

These are Eddy's alphabet blocks.
Trace over the letters.

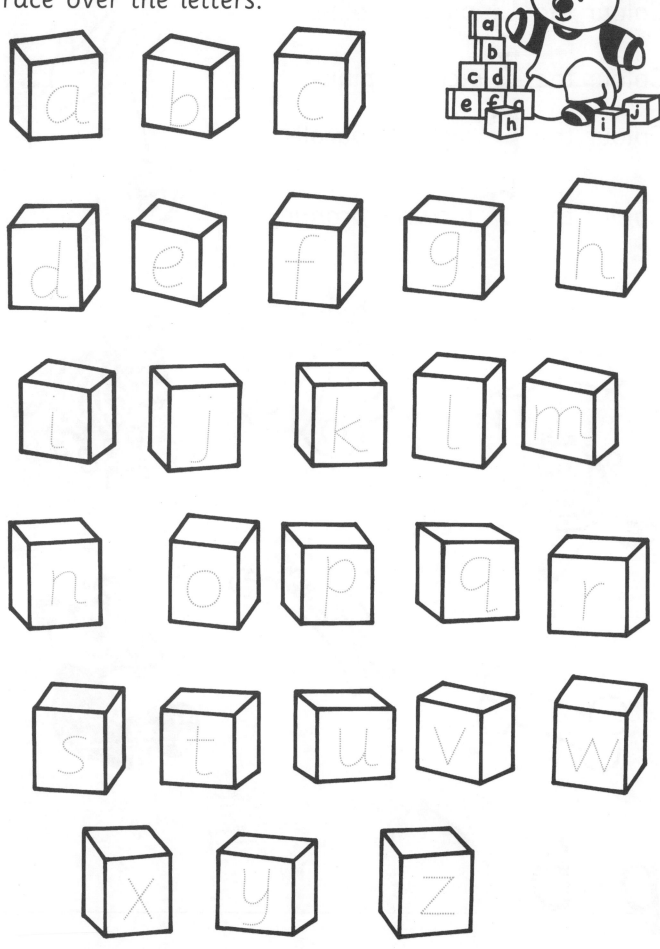

Draw lines to match each letter to the thing that begins with that letter.

r

g

l

m

j

d

j j j j j j j j

r l r l r l r l

m g m g m g m g

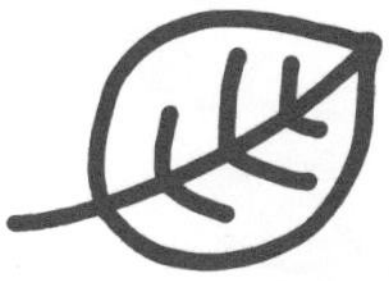

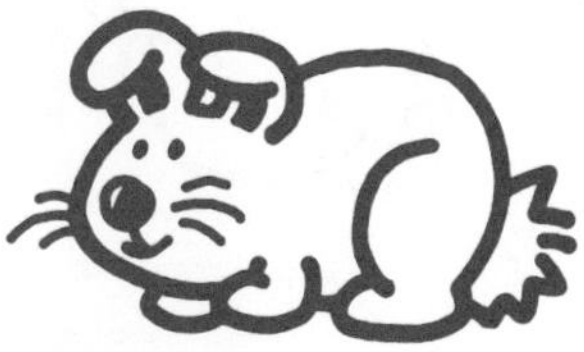

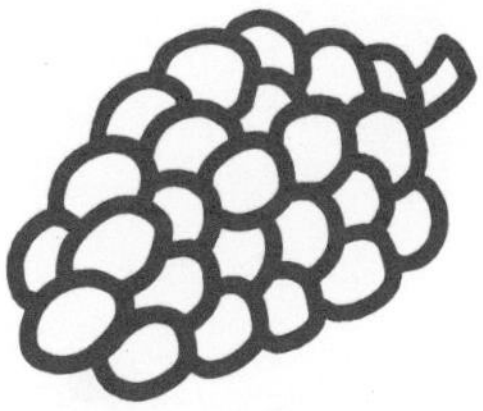

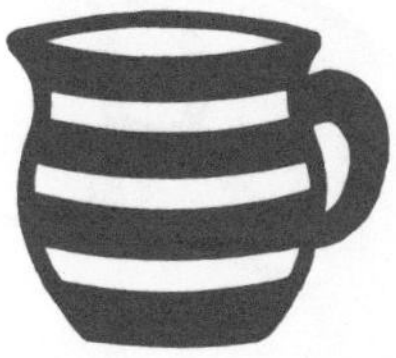

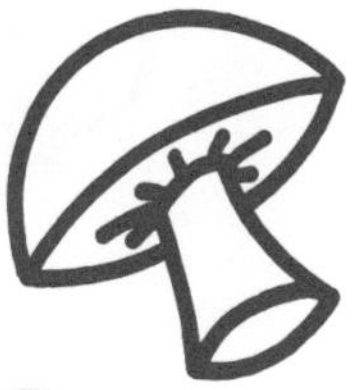

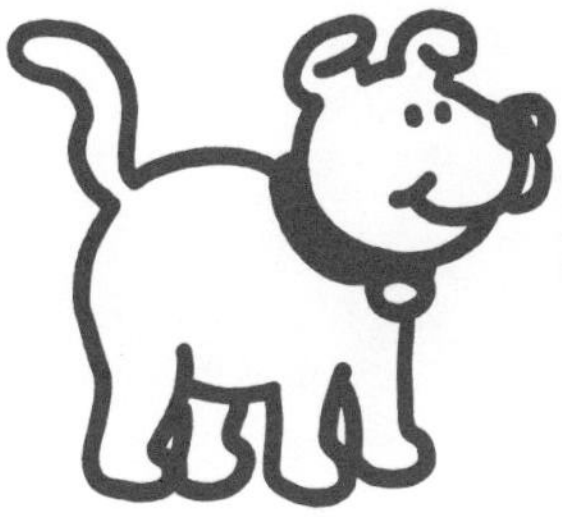

Eddy has found some letter ladybirds. Draw lines to match the letters to the ladybirds' letters.

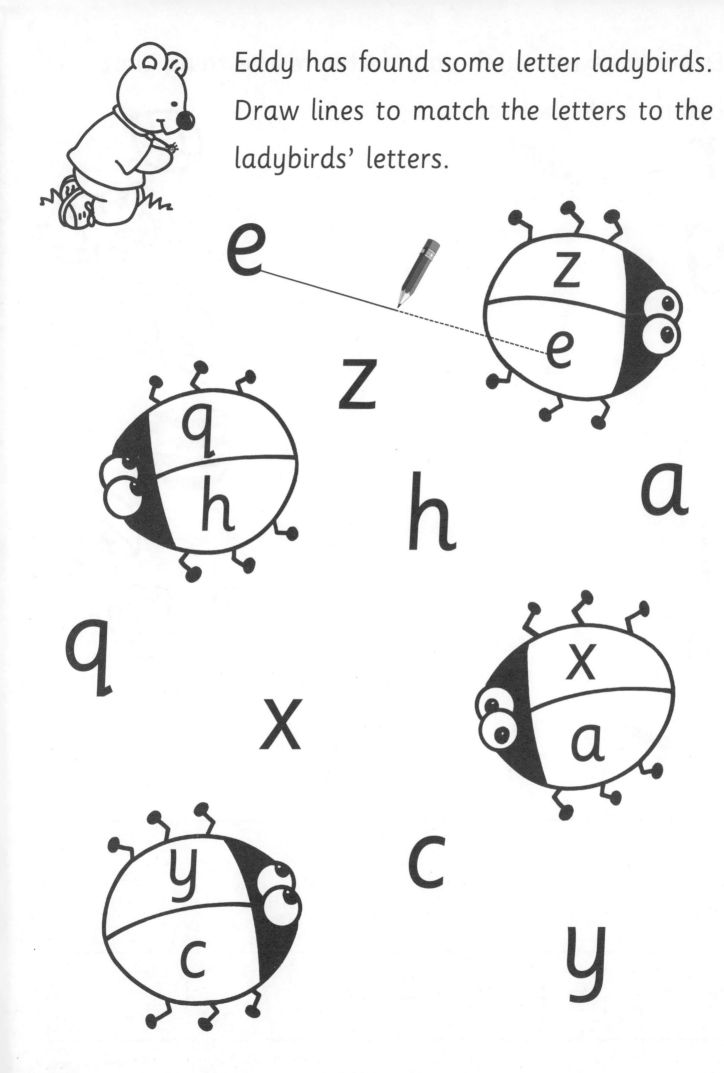

e

z

h

a

q

x

c

y

Look at the pictures and think of the start
of the words.

Colour the **q** pictures red.

Colour the **t** pictures green.

Colour the **h** pictures black.

Colour the **c** pictures purple.

Colour the **s** pictures yellow.

s

t h

Look at the picture and think of the word.
Write the first letter of the word in the box.

a b c d e

Look at the picture and think of the word.
Write the first letter of the word in the box.

f　　g　　h　　i　　j

Colour the picture on each line that starts with the sound.

d

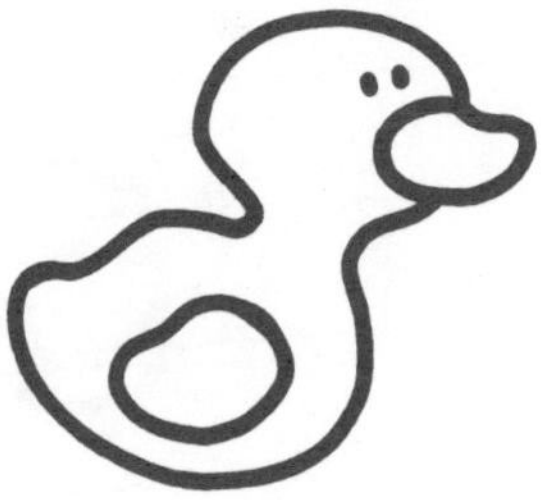

t

c

b

s

l

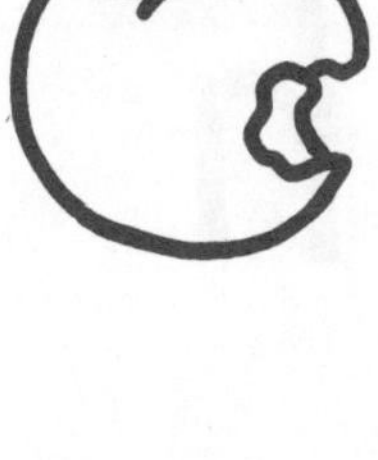

Draw lines to match each letter to the thing that starts with that letter.

Trace over the words in Eddy's garden.

Colour the picture.

Look at the picture and think of the word.

Draw a ring around the sound

which starts the word.

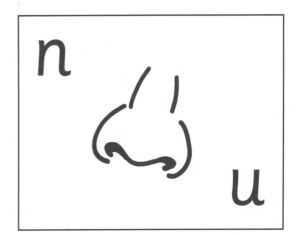

Eddy has made some flags.

Trace over the letter on each flag.

a b c

d e f g h i

j k l m n o

p q r s t u

v w x y z

Look at the pictures and think of the words.
Colour two pictures on each line that
match the starting sound.

Eddy says can you join the clouds with the same words?

window

window

flag

flag

queen

queen

rabbit

rabbit

Colour the pictures in each pair the same colour.

Eddy has drawn some pictures for you to colour.

All the words begin with **b** or **d**.
Trace over the words.

bicycle

dog

door

bed

duck

bird

bow

dress

21

Look at the word in the box.

Find another word the same in each line.

Draw a ring around it.

| bag | ant | bag | ant | ant | ant |

| car | sea | sea | sea | sea | car |

| gate | mat | mat | mat | gate | mat |

| tap | pan | tap | pan | pan | pan |

| day | sky | sky | day | sky | sky |

| man | zoo | man | zoo | zoo | zoo |

Trace over these words.

man

man   man

tap

tap   tap

dog

dog   dog

Eddy has written some words.

Draw a line to join the words that are the same.

Trace over these words.

fish fish fish fish

pig pig pig pig

Schofield & Sims
HELPING CHILDREN TO LEARN

Schofield & Sims was established in 1901 by two headmasters and since then our name has been synonymous with educationally sound texts and teaching materials. Our mission is to publish products which are:

- Educationally sound • Good value • Written by experienced teachers
- Extensively used in schools, nurseries and play groups
- Used by parents to support their children's learning

NURSERY WRITING BOOK 5

A series of six graded workbooks to aid the development of pre-reading and early writing skills, including left-to-right co-ordination, pencil control, visual perception, letter recognition, the alphabet, word recognition and word writing. Fun to do exercises reinforce and develop skills and understanding.

Nursery Writing Book 1 - 0 7217 0819 6
Nursery Writing Book 2 - 0 7217 0820 X
Nursery Writing Book 3 - 0 7217 0821 8
Nursery Writing Book 4 - 0 7217 0822 6
Nursery Writing Book 5 - 0 7217 0823 4
Nursery Writing Book 6 - 0 7217 0824 2

Schofield & Sims pre-school products for 4+ year olds

Posters
Sturdy, laminated posters, full colour, write-on/wipe-off, suitable for wall mounting or desk top use. Over 70 titles including the alphabet, numbers, colours, days, shapes, nursery rhymes, opposites, seasons, time, weather and our bodies.

Information
For further information about products for pre-school, Key Stage 1 and 2, please request our catalogue or visit our website at
www.schofieldandsims.co.uk

Nursery workbooks
Nursery Land
Books 1 - 4 **NEW**
A brand new series of workbooks packed with activities based on popular nursery rhymes, to help develop basic concepts and skills. Includes dot-to-dot, numbers 1-10, colour, shape, size, matching and odd one out.

Nursery Activity
Books 1 - 6
A gradual introduction to essential pre-reading and early mathematical skills through a series of graded workbooks. Each book includes lively exercises covering left-to-right co-ordination, sequencing, matching, colour recognition, shape and number recognition, counting and number writing practice.

Author   Kathryn Linaker
Illustrator   Linzi Henry
Cover design   Curve Creative - Bradford

First printed 1998
Reprinted 1998, 1999 (twice), 2000.

Printed by Hawthornes Printers, Nottingham

Schofield & Sims

Dogley Mill, Fenay Bridge, Huddersfield, HD8 0NQ
Phone 01484 607080   Fax 01484 606815

e-mail sales@schofieldandsims.co.uk

ISBN 0-7217-0823-4

9 780721 708232

Price £1.65
Pre-School
Age Range 4+ years